# BIGGEST BOOK OF SEARCH & FIND®

Tony and Tony Tallarico

Kidsbooks®

# FIND FREDDIE

Find Freddie along with hundreds of other
zany things in these hilarious scenes.

- ◎ Uncle Sam at the ballpark
- ◎ Cowboys on the beach
- ◎ Humpty Dumpty in Monsterville
- ◎ Flying fish in space
- ◎ Peanuts at the museum
- ◎ Rabbits at school
- ◎ Flying saucers in the Old West

. . . and lots more!

# Find Freddie
## at
# Home
### and...

- "8 Up" can
- Alarm clock
- Arrow
- Baseball player
- Baseball trophy
- Birdcage
- Bow tie
- Broken heart
- "Call Joe"
- Drum
- Elephant head
- Fake teeth
- Harmonica
- Hockey stick
- "How to Play" book
- "Junk Mail"
- Light switch
- Monster foot
- Orange-and-green lamp
- Paper airplanes (5)
- Peanuts
- Picture
- Popcorn
- Record
- Skulls (2)
- Straws (2)
- Sunglasses
- Telescope
- Thermometer
- Tire swing
- Yo-yo

# Find Freddie
## in
# Space
### and...

- Angel
- Balloon
- Basketball
- Bathtub
- Cannon
- Dogcatcher
- Doghouse
- Dragon
- Envelope
- Flying school bus
- Garbage truck
- Gorilla
- Hammer
- Mary Poppins
- Meatball
- "Meteor shower"
- NASA parachute
- Necktie
- Pencil
- Pink elephant
- Pinocchio
- "Planet of the Foot" (2)
- Polka-dot shorts
- Pyramid
- Red spray paint
- Rocking chair
- Scissors
- Slingshot
- Top hat
- Traffic light
- Trash can

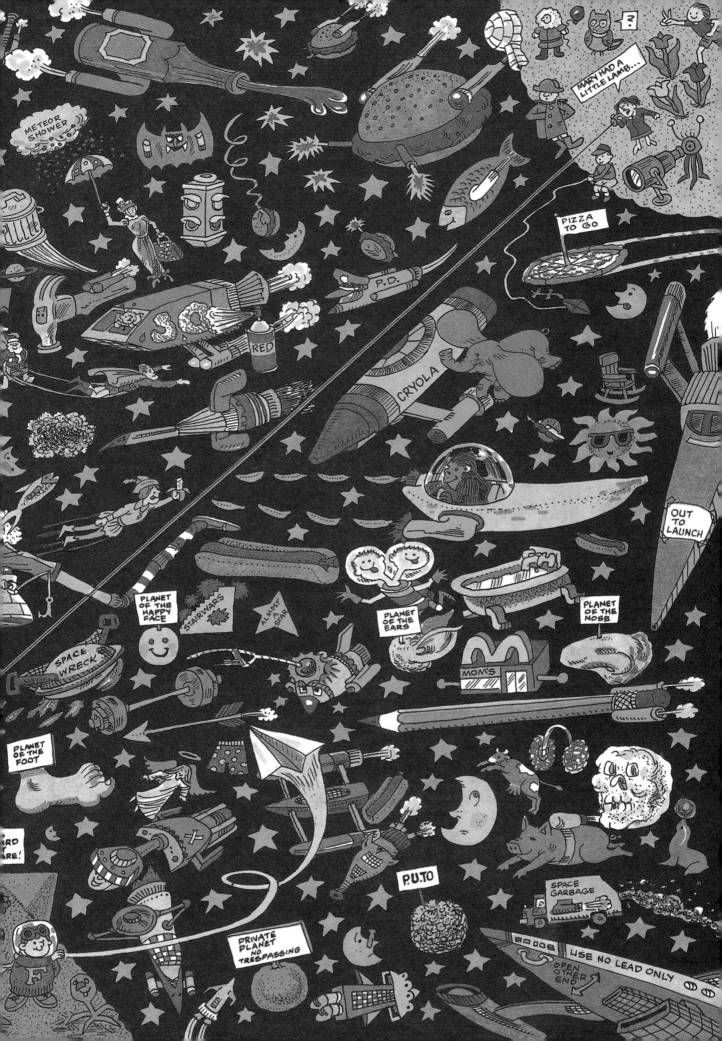

# Find Freddie at the Beach and...

# Find Freddie
## at
# School
### and...

- Air pump
- Barbells (2)
- Baseballs (2)
- Basketballs (3)
- Bench
- Briefcases (2)
- Broken windows (2)
- Butterfly net
- Cake
- Fish (2)
- Fishing pole
- Horse
- Jump rope
- Magic carpet
- Mail carrier
- Mouse
- Mud puddle
- Music notes (3)
- Paper airplanes (5)
- Pillow
- Pumpkin
- Rabbits (2)
- Skull
- Soccer ball
- Surfboard
- Swing set
- Telescope
- Trash can
- Tug-of-war
- Upside-down bucket

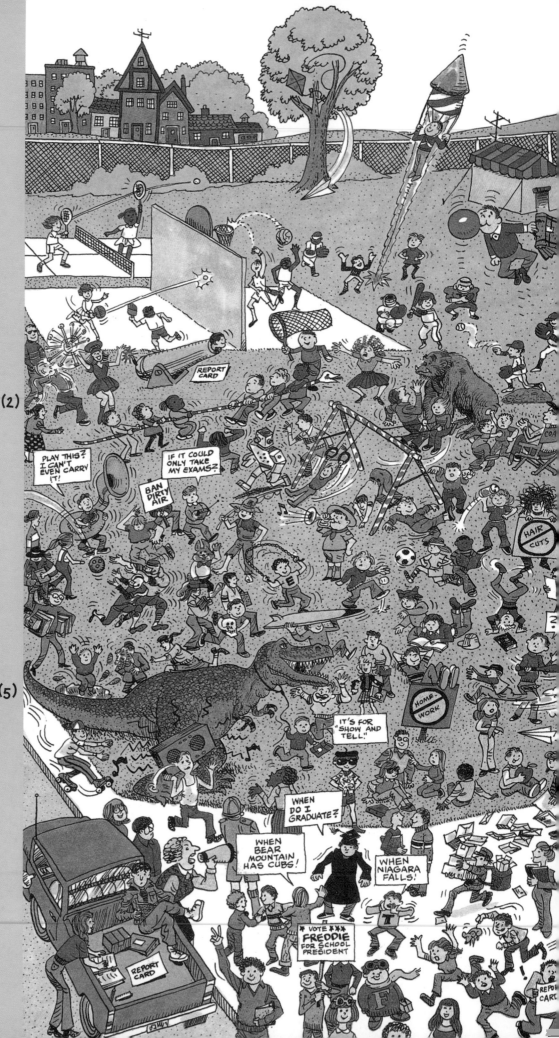

# Find Freddie on the
## School
## Bus Trip
### and...

- Barn
- Baseball bat
- Basketball court
- "Clean Me"
- Dogs (2)
- Elephant
- Flying bat
- Football
- Frankenstein's monster
- Giraffe
- Horse
- Hot dog mobile
- Jack-o'-lantern
- Moose head
- Pig
- Pizza truck
- Rowboat
- Santa Claus
- Scarecrow
- Snake
- Swimming pool
- Tennis court
- Tent
- Tic-tac-toe
- Tombstone
- Traffic cop
- Turtle
- Umbrellas (2)
- U-shaped building
- Well

# Find Freddie
in
# Monsterville
and...

- Broken heart
- Carrot
- Cowboy hat
- Flowers (2)
- "For Rent"
- Gorilla
- Hose
- Key
- Mouse hole
- Ms. Transylvania
- Mummy
- Number 13 (3)
- Octopus
- One-eyed monster
- Owl
- Parachute
- Pig
- Pile of bones
- Pink hand
- Pyramid
- Rat
- Scary trees (2)
- Skeleton
- Skulls (8)
- Stethoscope
- Three-legged ghost
- Tin can
- Tin man
- Trick-or-Treat bags (4)
- Weather vane

# Find Freddie at the **Airport** and...

- Binoculars
- Birdcage
- Chair
- Clothespins (6)
- Football
- Golf club
- Green checkered pants
- Guardhouse
- Hammock
- Harpoon
- Hearts (2)
- Helicopters (2)
- Hot-air balloon
- Hot dogs (2)
- Ice-cream cones (2)
- Kite
- Laundry line
- Locomotive
- Lost wallet
- Manhole
- Paint rollers (2)
- Parachute
- Pear
- "Pequod"
- Pizza
- Roller coaster
- Skier
- Stretch limo
- Submarine
- Toaster
- Wooden leg

# Find Freddie at the **Ballpark** and...

# Find **Freddie**
## at the
# **Museum**
### and...

- Airplane
- Alien
- Balloons (7)
- Bather
- Birdcage
- Birthday cake
- Doctor
- Doghouse
- Firefighter
- Fire hydrant
- "First Prize"
- Fishing pole
- Flying carpet
- Football player
- Guitar
- Headless man
- Hot-air balloon
- Ice-cream cone
- Jack-in-the-box
- Kite
- Knights (2)
- Long beard
- Magnifying glass
- Princess
- Quicksand
- Robin Hood
- Scuba diver
- Superman
- TV antenna
- Viking ship
- Watering can
- Whistle

# Find Freddie
## in the
# Old West
## Town
### and...

- Angel
- Apple
- Artist
- Baby turtle
- Camel
- Car
- Fire hydrant
- Fishing pole
- Flowerpot
- Football
- Guitar
- "ICU2"
- Monster hand
- Mouse holes (2)
- Outhouse
- Pencil
- Periscope
- Piano
- Pink elephant
- Rabbits (3)
- Sailboat
- Saw
- Smoke signal
- Soccer ball
- Stop sign
- Sun
- Toasters (5)
- UFO
- Umbrellas (2)
- Upside-down sign
- "Wet Paint"

FIND FREDDIE    LOOK FOR LISA    HUNT FOR HECTOR    SEARCH FOR SAM

WHERE ARE THEY?

# HUNT FOR HECTOR

Where's Hector?
You'll have to search through these
wacky scenes—and more—to find him!

- Cats at the Dog Mall
- K-9 secret agents
- Fencing dogs at the Olympics
- Fire hydrants in Dogtown
- Bones at the Hall of Fame
- Dancing dogs at school
- Hot dogs in space

. . . and lots more!

# Hunt for Hector at the Dog Hall of Fame and...

- Baby kangaroo
- "Bach Beagle"
- Beard
- Birds (2)
- Chef
- Dog bowl
- Dogcatcher
- Dog stamp
- Elephant
- Eyeglasses (3)
- Fire hydrant
- Football helmet
- Hearts (3)
- Hot-air balloon
- Kangaroo
- Mailbag
- Moon
- Mouse hole
- Music note
- Oversized tie
- Pilgrim hat
- Police dogs (2)
- Space dog
- Stamp
- Stars (20)
- Stool
- Target
- Top hat
- Umpire

# Hunt for Hector at Dog School and...

# Hunt for **Hector** among the **Dogcatchers** and...

- Airplane
- Barber pole
- Bathing dog
- Briefcase
- Car antenna
- Cats (5)
- Convertible car
- Dog bowls (3)
- "Dog mail"
- Dollar signs (11)
- Empty bowls (2)
- Fire hose
- Fire hydrants (4)
- Fire truck
- Fishing pole
- Guitar
- Heart
- Manhole
- Music note
- Net
- Piano
- Pink hats (8)
- Rope swing
- Satellite dish
- Shower
- Sirens (2)
- Tree
- Turtle
- "UDS"
- Umbrella
- Watermelon
- Water tower

# Hunt for Hector
where the
## Rich and Famous
## Dogs Live
### and...

- Admiral
- Alligator
- Artist
- "Big Wheel"
- Bird bath
- Blimp
- Bone chimney
- Candle
- Castle
- Cat
- Cooks (2)
- Crown
- Dog fish
- Dog flag
- Fire hydrant
- Golfers (2)
- Guard
- Heart
- Heron
- Human
- Joggers (3)
- Periscope
- Pillow
- Pool
- Sipping a soda
- Star
- Tennis player
- Umbrella
- Violinist
- Water-skier
- Whale

# Hunt for **Hector** at the **K-9 Clean up** and...

# Hunt for Hector
## at the
# Super Dog Bowl
### and...

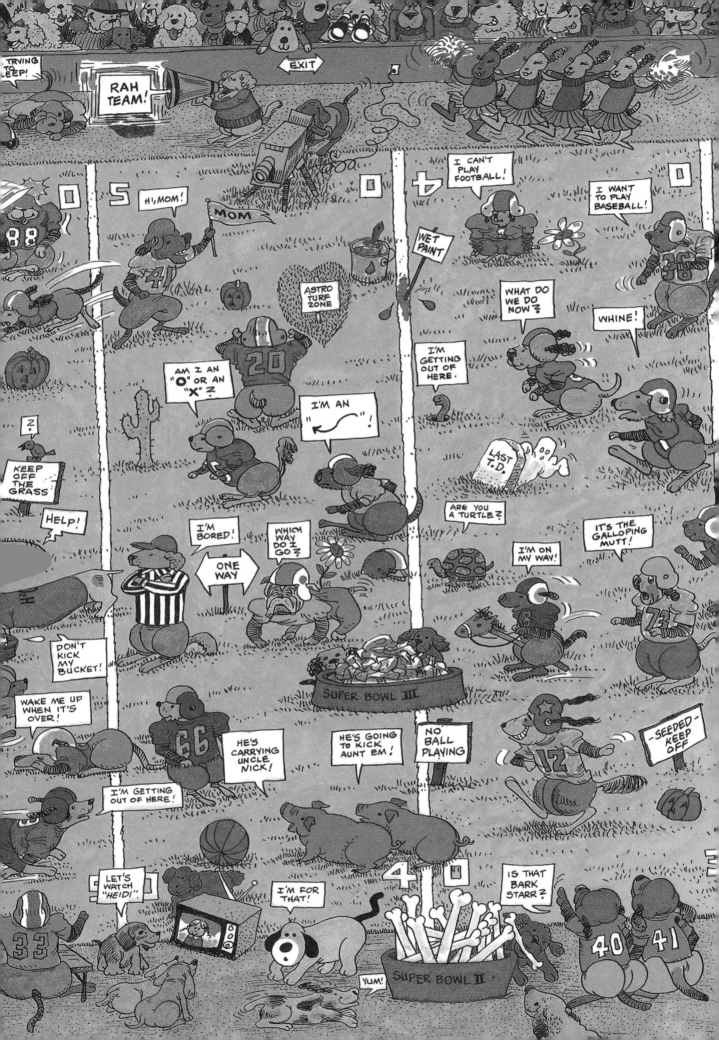

# Hunt for Hector at the Dog Mall and...

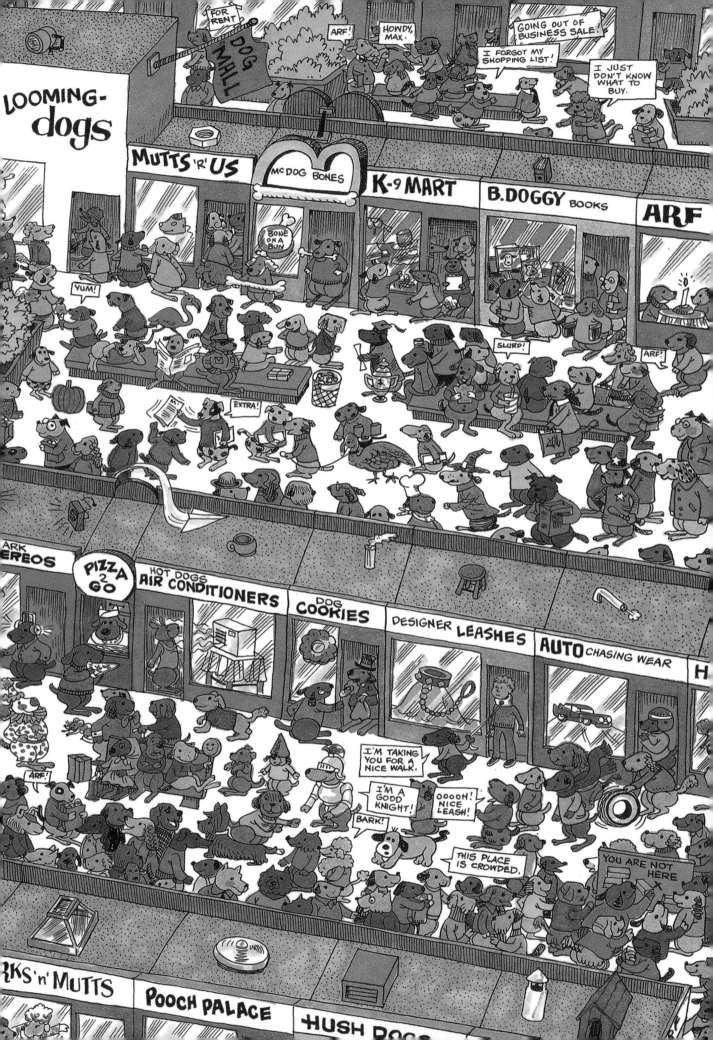

# Hunt for **Hector** at the **Dog Olympics** and...

- Bone bat
- Bow
- Bowling ball
- Broom
- Bucket
- Clipboard
- Diving board
- Fallen skater
- Fencing swords (2)
- Fishing pole
- Football players (3)
- Golf tee
- Hat with propeller
- Home plate
- Ice skates (14)
- Karate dog
- Ping-Pong paddle
- Pitcher
- Pole-vaulter
- Race car
- Ski jumper
- Stop sign
- Target
- Tennis racket
- Top hat
- Trainer
- TV camera
- Volleyball
- Weight lifter
- Yo-yo

# Hunt for Hector at the TV Quiz Show and...

# Hunt for Hector
## in
## Space
### and...

# Hunt for Hector
## in
# Dogtown
### and...

HUNT FOR HECTOR    SEARCH FOR SAM    FIND FREDDIE    LOOK FOR LISA

# LOOK FOR LISA

Look for Lisa in all sorts of crazy places!
While you're looking,
you'll see crazy things, such as:

- Hippos at a rock concert
- Cactuses on the beach
- Parrots in the library
- Surfers on a farm
- Frogs at the flea market
- Snow White at the marathon
- Unicorns in Utah

. . . and much, much more!

# Look for **Lisa** at the **Marathon** and...

- Angel
- Barrel
- Basketball
- Bucket
- Cane
- Chef
- Cowboy
- Deer
- Diving board
- Doctor
- Elephants (2)
- Ice-cream cone
- Kite
- Motorcycle
- Musical notes (3)
- Net
- Octopus
- Periscope
- Policeman
- Rocket
- Roller skates
- Sad face
- Scooter
- "Shortcut"
- Sombrero
- Speed skater
- Spotted dog
- Strongman
- Surfer
- Taxi
- Tuba
- Umbrella

## Look for Lisa
# After School
### and...

## Look for Lisa at the Rock Concert and...

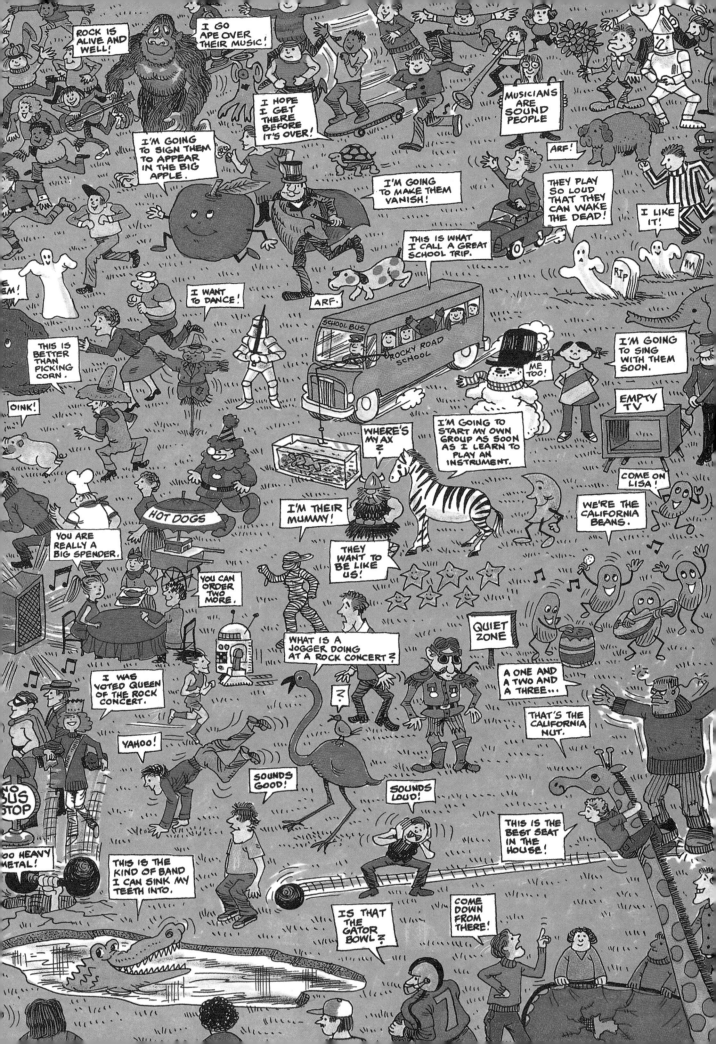

# Look for Lisa on the
# Farm
### and...

- Cactus
- Cave
- Clouds (3)
- Donkey
- "Don't Stop" sign
- Egg
- Elephant
- Eskimo
- Finish line
- Fox
- Ghost
- Giant pumpkin
- "Grade A"
- Horses (3)
- Lion
- Log pile
- Message in a bottle
- Net
- Periscope
- Pitchfork
- Policeman
- Prisoner
- Rowboat
- Scuba diver
- Stop sign
- "Summer"
- Surfboards (2)
- Tent
- Turkey
- Water bucket
- Weather vane

## Look for **Lisa** at the **Beach** and...

- Artist
- Beach ball
- Broom
- Bunch of balloons
- Cactus (4)
- Castle
- Cello
- Crocodile
- Cruise ship
- Diving board
- Hearts (3)
- Horse
- Jack-in-the-box
- Kite
- Lifeguard
- Lost swim trunks
- Magnifying glass
- Merman
- Palm trees (3)
- Pickle barrel
- Policeman
- Sailboat
- Sailors (2)
- Sea serpent
- Seahorse
- Starfish (9)
- Swans (2)
- Telescope
- Trash can
- Tricycle
- Turtle
- Whale

# Look for Lisa at the Big Sale and...

- Balloon
- Clothespins (9)
- Count Dracula
- Disappearing men (2)
- "Don't Stop Shopping"
- Flower hat
- Football
- Football helmet
- Gumball machine
- Hard hat
- Janitor
- Kite
- Magic mirror
- Manhole cover
- Octopus
- Paint can
- Paper airplane
- Pig
- Pogo stick
- Polka-dot shorts
- Rabbit
- Rain slicker
- Rat
- Robot
- Roller skates
- Shirtless shopper
- Ski jump
- Skis (8)
- Teddy bear
- Turtle

## Look for Lisa around the World and...

- Airplane
- Castle
- Cruise ship
- Elephant
- Fisherman
- Flamingo
- Foot
- Golf club
- Guitar
- Horse
- Hot-air balloon
- Ladder
- Lighthouse
- Lion
- Movie camera
- Penguins (6)
- Pine trees (6)
- Pizza man
- Refrigerator
- Sailboats (4)
- Santa Claus
- Scarves (2)
- Seal
- Sea monster
- Skis (8)
- Sombrero
- Submarine
- Surfboards (3)
- Television
- UFOs (2)
- Walrus
- Whale

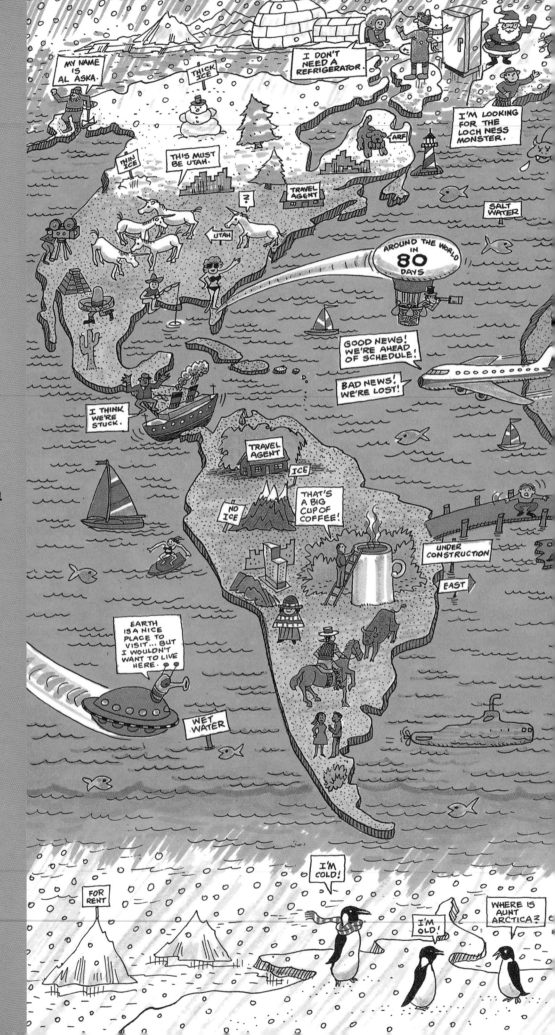

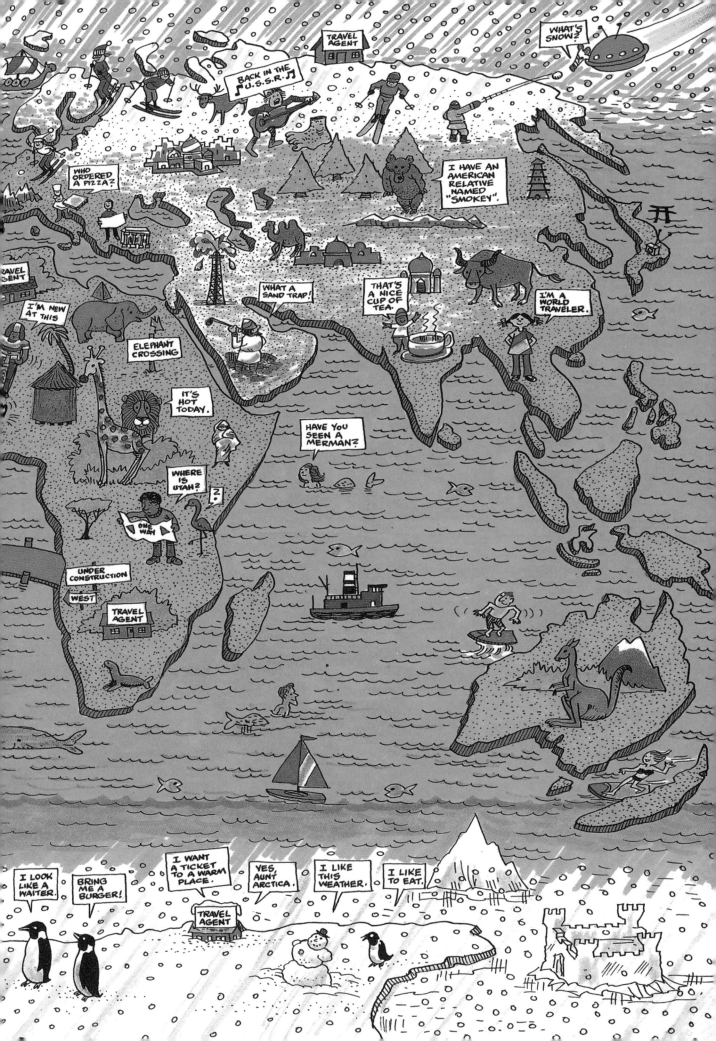

# Look for **Lisa** at the **Library** and...

- Baseball
- Birdcage
- Bowling pins (10)
- Brooms (2)
- Cactus
- Cactus book
- Cake
- Campfire
- Candle
- Car
- Football player
- Frying pan
- Globe
- Hamburger
- Hearts (4)
- Hockey stick
- Hot dog
- Jack-in-the-box
- Knight
- Monster hands (3)
- Music note
- Napoleon
- Old tire
- Pole-vaulter
- Policewoman
- "Quiet" signs (6)
- Smiley face
- Teapot
- Trap door
- Tricycle
- Wagon
- Witch

# Look for Lisa at the Amusement Park and...

- All-north weather vane
- Archer
- Cheese
- Clock
- Clowns (3)
- Cowboys (2)
- Crocodile
- Crooked chimney
- Diving board
- Dollar sign
- Fishing pole
- Heads without bodies (2)
- Ice block
- Manhole
- Moon
- Mouse hole
- Mummy
- Pear
- Snowman
- Space explorer
- Tent
- Tied-up man
- Tin man
- Tombstones (3)
- "Tunnel of Love"
- Umbrella
- Witch
- Wristwatches (7)

## Look for **Lisa** at the **Flea Market** and...

- Birdcages (2)
- Clown doll
- Court jester
- Cowboy hat
- Crown
- Elephant
- Elf
- Fish (3)
- Fishing hook
- "Flea Market Map"
- Football
- Golf club
- Graduate
- Horse
- Monster hand
- Necklace
- Old tire
- Paintbrush
- Pear
- Records (8)
- Saddle
- Sailor hat
- Scuba diver
- Shopping bag
- Skateboard
- Telephone booth
- Train conductor
- Trumpet
- Wheelbarrow
- Witch

## Look for Lisa as the
# Circus Comes to Town
### and...

LOOK FOR LISA    FIND FREDDIE    SEARCH FOR SAM    HUNT FOR HECTOR

# SEARCH FOR SAM

WHERE ARE THEY?

Sam's a sly cat, so good luck in your search!
You'll encounter hilarious characters in strange
scenes as you search for Sam.

- Dogs at the cat show
- Rhinos at the disco
- Alley cats in ancient Egypt
- Meows at midnight
- Fat cats at the gym
- Sharks in Cat City
- Dogbusters

. . . and lots more!

# Search for Sam
## in
# Cat City
### and...

# Search for Sam
## on
# Friday the 13th
### and...

# Search for Sam
## at
# Fat Cat Gym
### and...

# Search for Sam at the
# Midnight Meowing
### and...

- Baseball
- Baseball bat
- Birdhouse
- Can
- Cannon
- Cloud
- Egg
- Fishbowl
- Fish skeletons (2)
- Football
- Gate
- Jack-o'-lantern
- Light
- Microphone
- Moon
- "No Welcome"
- mat
- Old tire
- Piggy bank
- Police car
- Policeman
- Pot
- Record player
- Rolling pin
- Spoon
- Stacks of paper (2)
- Stars (4)
- Table
- Tent
- UFO
- Wood planks (3)

# Search for Sam at the Disco and...

- Ballerina
- Blue rhinos (2)
- Breakdance cat
- Cat blowing horn
- Chef
- Clipboard
- Clown cat
- Cowboy cat
- Disco ball
- Doctor
- Dog
- Duck
- Earplug seller
- Earrings
- Eye patch
- Flowerpot
- Hard hat
- Karate cat
- Lampshade
- Pig
- Pirate sword
- Pizza
- Police officer
- Record player
- Roller skates
- Skis
- Snow cat
- Speakers (10)
- Sunglasses
- Swinging cat
- Top hat
- Wooden leg

# Search for Sam
## at the
# Battle of Cats and Mice
### and...

# Search for Sam
## in
# Ancient Egypt
### and...

# Search for Sam at the **Cat Show** and...

- Ball of yarn
- Banjo
- Beach chair
- Bib
- Bones (2)
- Broom
- Camera
- Coconuts (2)
- Cow
- Cracked wall
- Cymbals (2)
- Fish bones (4)
- Fishing pole
- Graduate
- Guitar
- Hearts (3)
- Joggers (2)
- Lion
- Man in a cat suit
- Net
- Newspaper
- Palm tree
- Pizza boxes (2)
- Pool
- Scarf
- Sombrero
- Red bow
- Red curtain
- Royal cat
- Ticket booth
- Tombstone
- Witch

## Search for **Sam** with the **Dogbusters** and...

- ○ Balloon
- ○ Birdhouse
- ○ Bones (13)
- ○ Bridge
- ○ Broom
- ○ Clown
- ○ Crane
- ○ Crocodile
- ○ Detective
- ○ Dogs in tree (2)
- ○ Fish (4)
- ○ Flag
- ○ Flower
- ○ Hollow log
- ○ Horse
- ○ Jack-o'-lantern
- ○ Ladders (3)
- ○ Lamppost
- ○ Manhole cover
- ○ Old tire
- ○ Pizza box
- ○ Saddle
- ○ Sailboat
- ○ Siren
- ○ Surfboard
- ○ Taxi
- ○ Tent
- ○ Tightrope walker
- ○ Turtle
- ○ Umbrella
- ○ Wanted poster
- ○ Witch

# Search for Sam at the North Pole and...

- Badge
- Bells (2)
- Bread
- Broken chair
- Cactus
- Campfire
- Chef's hat
- Clock
- Fish
- Fishing pole
- Football
- Globe
- Green sock
- Hammer
- Kite
- Locomotive
- Miner's hat
- Music notes (3)
- Ornament
- Pizza
- Polar bear
- Reindeer
- Satellite dish
- Singing birds (2)
- Skier
- Snake with a hat
- Stepladder
- Toy car
- Yo-yo
- Zebras (2)

SEARCH FOR SAM  FIND FREDDIE  HUNT FOR HECTOR  LOOK FOR LISA

# DETECT DONALD

# Detect Donald at the Cheez-E Diner and...

- Bear
- Bowling ball
- Dinosaur
- Dog
- Ear of corn
- Earrings (3)
- Elf
- Eye patch
- Frankenstein's monster
- Ghost
- King
- Knight in armor
- Leaf
- Menus (2)
- Parrot
- Pot
- Raccoon hat
- Sailor hat
- Shark
- Skeleton
- Slice of watermelon
- Snake
- Straw
- Sunglasses (2)
- Watch

# Detect Donald in Colonial America and...

- Antenna
- Baseball
- Basket
- Bell
- Ben Franklin
- Betsy Ross
- Bone
- Broom
- Bucket
- Candles (2)
- Cannonballs (4)
- Cats (2)
- Chicken
- Clock
- Dogs (2)
- Drums (3)
- Duck
- Ear of corn
- Flower vase
- Horses (4)
- Kites (2)
- Lamppost
- Mouse
- One dollar bill
- Saw
- Spinning wheel

# Detect Donald in the Middle Ages and...

# Detect Donald
## in
# Cartoonland
### and...

- Banana peel
- Baseball bats (2)
- Bees (4)
- Broom
- Burst balloon
- Chicken
- Crow
- Elephants (2)
- Elf
- Firefighter
- Flower
- Gingerbread man
- Golf tee
- Horses (2)
- Hot dog
- Lamp
- Masks (2)
- Mushroom
- Pie
- Pirate hat
- Pot
- Rabbit
- Sandwich
- Saxophone
- Scarf
- Snake
- Swiss cheese
- Underwear

# Detect **Donald**
## at the
# Pirates'
# Battle
### and...

# Detect Donald
in the
## Future
### and...

# Detect Donald in
# Napoleon's France
### and...

# Detect Donald
## at
# Fort Knocks
### and...

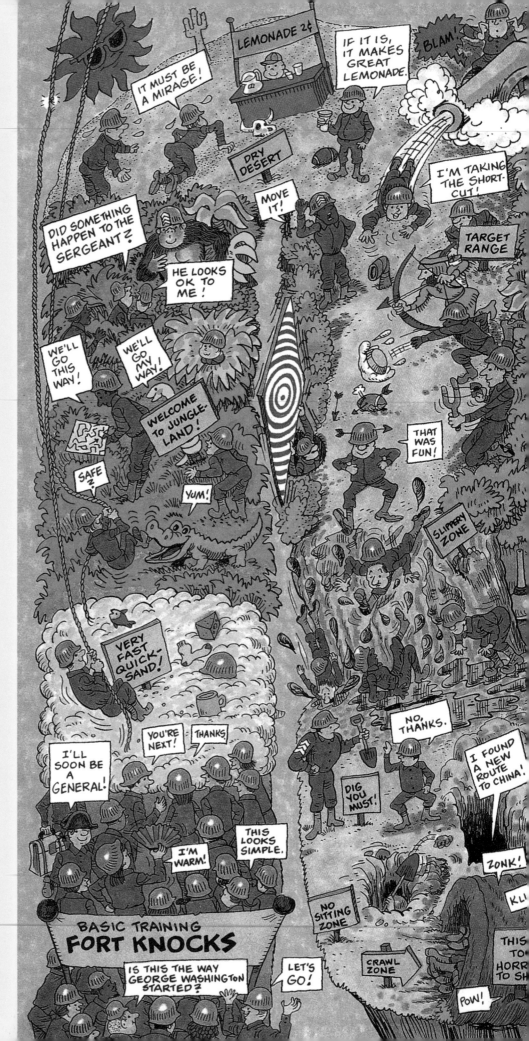

# Detect Donald
## in
# Ancient Rome
### and...

- Arrow
- Backwards helmet
- Balloon
- Cactus
- Caesar
- Cat
- Falling rock
- Flower
- Horseless chariot
- Jack-o'-lantern
- Julius and Augustus
- Kite
- Mask
- Painted egg
- Pig
- Pizza box
- Puddles (2)
- Rabbit
- Shield
- Skull
- Slice of pizza
- Snake
- Sock
- Spears (2)
- Star
- Underwear

# Detect Donald
## in
# Prehistoric Times
### and...

LOOK FOR LAURA  DETECT DONALD  FIND FRANKIE  SEARCH FOR SUSIE

# Find Frankie at the Monster Club Meeting and...

# Find Frankie on the **Street** and...

- Benches (2)
- Books (2)
- Candle
- Clowns (2)
- Crayon
- Crowns (2)
- Dogs (2)
- Dripping faucet
- Duck
- Fish
- Flower hat
- Flowerpots (2)
- Handbag
- Hard hat
- Jogger
- Mouse ears
- Newspaper
- Parrot
- Peanut
- Pinocchio
- Postal worker
- Sailor hats (2)
- Sombrero
- Spaceman
- Suspenders (3 sets)
- Tepee
- Toolbox
- Umbrella

# Find Frankie
in the
## Supermarket
and...

- Bandanas (3)
- Bare foot
- Broom
- Cobweb
- Cook
- Cowboy
- Crown
- Dog fish
- Eggs
- Firefighter
- Fire hydrant
- Fishing pole
- Football player
- Handbag
- Jack-in-the-box
- Knee pads
- Paddles (2)
- Pear
- People sleeping (2)
- Pocket watch
- Pole-vaulter
- Propeller
- Scarves (2)
- Snake
- Straw
- Sunglasses
- Swordfish
- Toaster

# Find Frankie at the **Theater** and...

# Find Frankie at the Zoo and...

# Find Frankie at the
# Rowdy Roller Rink
### and...

- Arrow
- Baby
- Balloons (3)
- Bird
- Buffalo
- Cactus
- Candle
- Clowns (2)
- Deer
- Dogs (3)
- Fairy godmother
- Green flag
- Hamburger
- Jester hat
- Jump rope
- Knight
- Lamp shade
- Manhole
- Mouse
- Paintbrushes (2)
- "Pigman"
- Pizza
- Robot
- Sheep
- Sombrero
- Suspenders
- Tennis racket

# Find Frankie in the **Arcade** and...

# Find Frankie
## in the
# Suburbs
### and...

- Basketball
- Bone
- Books (3)
- Broken window
- Broom
- "Dead End"
- Flying bat
- Gate
- Ghost
- Golf bag
- Guitar
- Hammock
- Haunted house
- Jogger
- Jump rope
- Mailbox
- Mail delivery
- Monster hands (2)
- Mouse
- Rabbit
- Shovel
- Snake
- Sunglasses
- Superhero
- Tea bag
- Tire swing
- Trash cans (3)
- Tuba

# Find Frankie at the Monsters' New Clubhouse and...

- Bee
- Broom
- Candles (2)
- Clouds (2)
- Cobweb
- Doormat
- Flower
- Football
- Heart
- Light bulb
- Mouse hole
- Mustache
- Neckties (2)
- Octopus
- Pirate
- Pointed hats (2)
- Sled
- Smiling ghosts (2)
- Smiling star
- Snake
- Thirteens (4)
- Tic-tac-toe
- Tiny monster
- Trapdoor
- Trees (2)
- Turtle
- Umbrella

FIND FRANKIE    SEARCH FOR SUSIE    LOOK FOR LAURA    DETECT DONALD

# LOOK FOR LAURA

# Look for Laura on the Planet Maxxx and...

- ○ Asteroid for rent
- ○ Banana
- ○ Baseball
- ○ Birds (2)
- ○ Briefcase
- ○ Broom
- ○ Clocks (4)
- ○ Duck
- ○ Footballs (2)
- ○ Fork
- ○ Hammer
- ○ Helmet
- ○ Horse
- ○ Hot dog
- ○ Monkey
- ○ Moon
- ○ Mushroom
- ○ Paper airplane
- ○ Plumber's plunger
- ○ Pyramid
- ○ Robot
- ○ Skateboard
- ○ Snake
- ○ Star
- ○ Sunglasses
- ○ Tire
- ○ Tree

# Look for **Laura** in the **Ocean** and...

# Look for Laura at the
# Watering Hole
### and...

- Baby bird
- Birdcage
- Briefcase
- Clothespins (2)
- Coconuts (4)
- Donkey
- Duck
- Feather
- Fish (3)
- Giraffe
- Headband
- Heart
- Hippo
- Leopard
- Lions (2)
- Log
- Lollipop
- Octopus
- Ping-Pong paddle
- Radio
- Rhinoceros
- Robot
- Snake
- Turtle
- TV set
- Worm

# Look for Laura
### on a
# Ski Slope
### in the Alps
### and...

- Balloon
- Barrels (2)
- Car
- Duck
- Earmuffs (3 pairs)
- Easel
- Elephant
- Frankenstein's monster
- Glove
- Headbands (2)
- Lamppost
- Lost boots (2)
- Lost ski
- Red bows (3)
- Scarves (7)
- Scuba diver
- Shovel
- "Soft Snow"
- Sunbather
- Telephone
- Telescope
- Tent
- Thrown snowball
- Train
- Tree

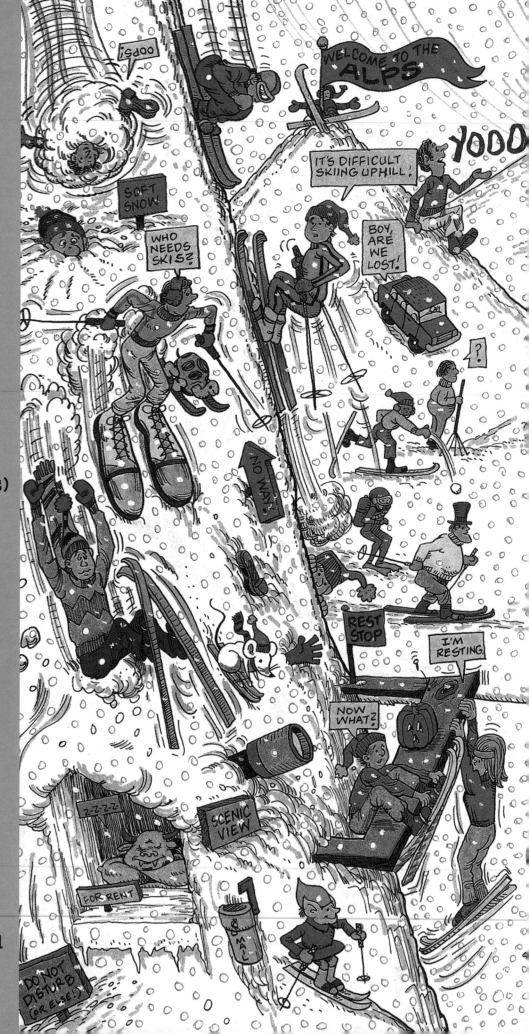

## Look for Laura at the Bah-ha Bazaar and...

- Beach ball
- Broom
- Cat
- Clouds (2)
- Coconuts (4)
- Donkey
- Elephant
- Flying carpets (2)
- Football
- Genie
- Horn
- Ice-cream cone
- Igloo
- Kite
- Necklace
- Oil well
- Pillow fight
- Rabbit
- Shovel
- Skier
- Snail
- Snakes (4)
- Straw baskets (2)
- Sunglasses
- Telescope
- Tents (4)

# Look for Laura in Europe and...

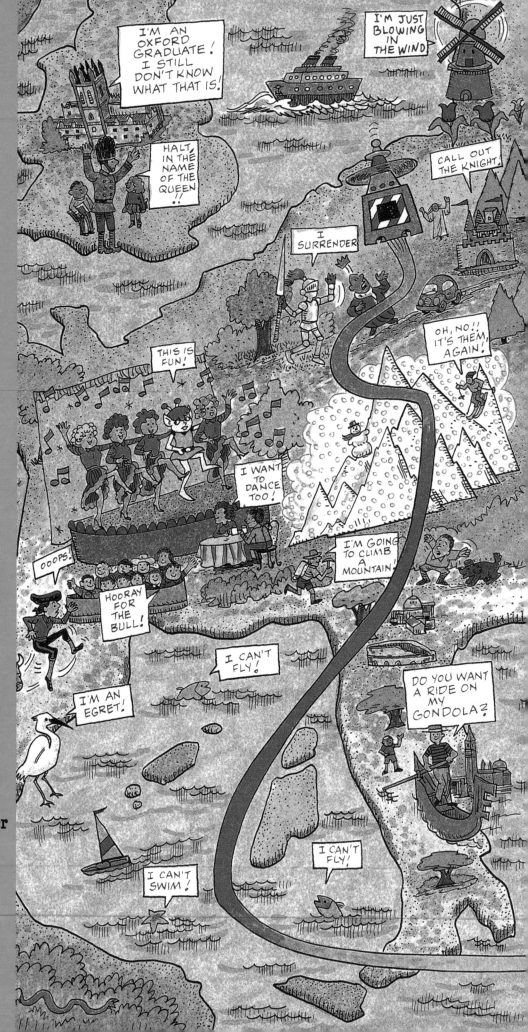

# Look for Laura at the Circus and...

## Look for Laura in Washington DC and...

# Look for Laura
## at
# School
### and...

# Look for **Laura** at the **Welcome Home Party** and...

- Balloons (2)
- Baseball
- Boot
- Bouquet of flowers
- Bowling ball
- Broom
- Dog
- Donut
- Fish
- Flowerpot
- Half-moons (2)
- Hearts (2)
- Ice-cream cone
- Manhole
- Nose
- Old tire
- Paddle
- Pail
- Pocket watch
- Scissors
- Screwdriver
- Stars (8)
- Straw
- Sunglasses
- Swiss cheese
- Top hat
- Turtle

DETECT DONALD    FIND FRANKIE    SEARCH FOR SUSIE    LOOK FOR LAURA

# SEARCH FOR SUSIE

# Search for Susie
at the
# Water
## Ride
and...

- Apple
- Beach ball
- Bib
- Bull
- Candles (2)
- Cats (2)
- Earring
- Elephants (2)
- Fishing pole
- Gorilla
- Hearts (2)
- Hot dog
- Kangaroo
- Paper bag
- Parrot
- Pencil
- Periscope
- Picnic basket
- Pitcher
- Puddles (4)
- Rabbits (2)
- Scuba diver
- Sheep
- Snakes (2)
- Sunglasses (2)
- Tents (3)
- Tire

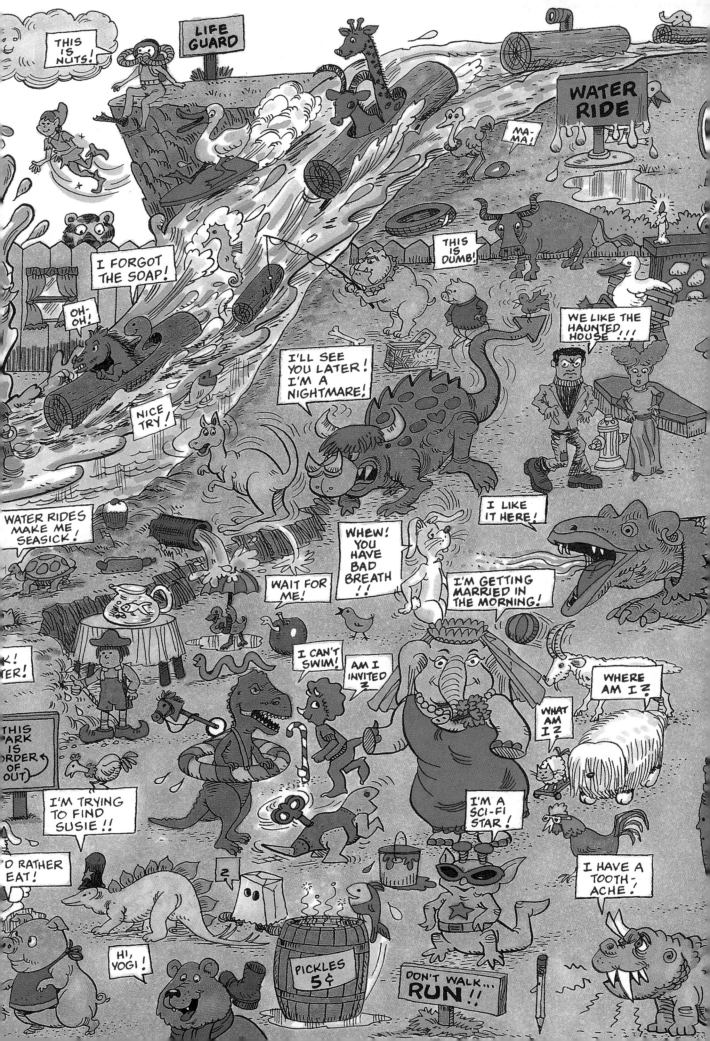

# Search for Susie at the Carousel and...

- ○ Baseball bat
- ○ Baseball caps (3)
- ○ Beach ball
- ○ Bench
- ○ Butterfly
- ○ Ear of corn
- ○ Earring
- ○ Elephants (5)
- ○ Fish (2)
- ○ Flowerpots (2)
- ○ Football
- ○ Giraffe
- ○ Hammer
- ○ Handbags (2)
- ○ Ice-cream cone
- ○ Magnifying glass
- ○ Mouse hole
- ○ Paintbrush
- ○ Panda
- ○ Rabbits (3)
- ○ Sailboat
- ○ Scarf
- ○ Seal
- ○ Spoon
- ○ Stork
- ○ Straw
- ○ Telescope
- ○ Train engine

# Search for Susie at the Fun House and...

# Search for Susie at the Ferris Wheel and...

- Alarm clock
- Barrel
- Broken eggs
- Coffeepot
- Dog
- Ducks (3)
- Elephant
- Football
- Giraffe
- Gorilla
- Guitar
- Happy face
- Helicopter
- Jack-o'-lantern
- Jeep
- Ladders (2)
- Lions (2)
- Lost sneaker
- Mice (2)
- Neckties (4)
- Owl
- Paintbrushes (2)
- Popcorn
- Quicksand
- Shovel
- Snake
- Telephone

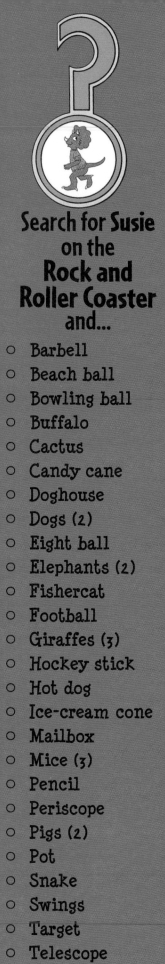

# Search for **Susie** on the **Rock and Roller Coaster** and...

- Barbell
- Beach ball
- Bowling ball
- Buffalo
- Cactus
- Candy cane
- Doghouse
- Dogs (2)
- Eight ball
- Elephants (2)
- Fishercat
- Football
- Giraffes (3)
- Hockey stick
- Hot dog
- Ice-cream cone
- Mailbox
- Mice (3)
- Pencil
- Periscope
- Pigs (2)
- Pot
- Snake
- Swings
- Target
- Telescope
- Tin can
- Train engine

# Search for Susie
in the
# Game
# Room
### and...

- Banana
- Blindfold
- Bucket
- Cat
- Catcher's mitt
- Donkeys (2)
- "Don't Be Quiet"
- Dustpan
- Fake nose
- Flying reptile
- Football
- Graduate's hat
- Green bug
- Guitar
- Hairbrush
- Juggler
- Kangaroo
- Mouse house
- Picture frame
- Pie
- Rabbits (3)
- Ring toss
- Roller skate
- Sailboat
- Scarf
- Snake
- Toolbox

## Search for Susie on the Bumper Cars and...

# Search for Susie at the Ice Cream Shop and...

- Alien
- Banana peel
- Bowling ball
- Bubble gum
- Cactus
- Camel
- Candy cane
- Can of paint
- Clown
- Cow
- Flowerpot
- Flying carpet
- Flying reptiles (2)
- Football helmet
- Mice (3)
- Nail
- Parrot
- Pig
- Pillow
- Pocket watch
- Propeller hat
- Rocking horse
- Sailor hat
- Shovel
- Snake
- Star
- Straw

# Search for Susie on the Giant Swings and...

SEARCH FOR SUSIE   LOOK FOR LAURA   DETECT DONALD   FIND FRANKIE

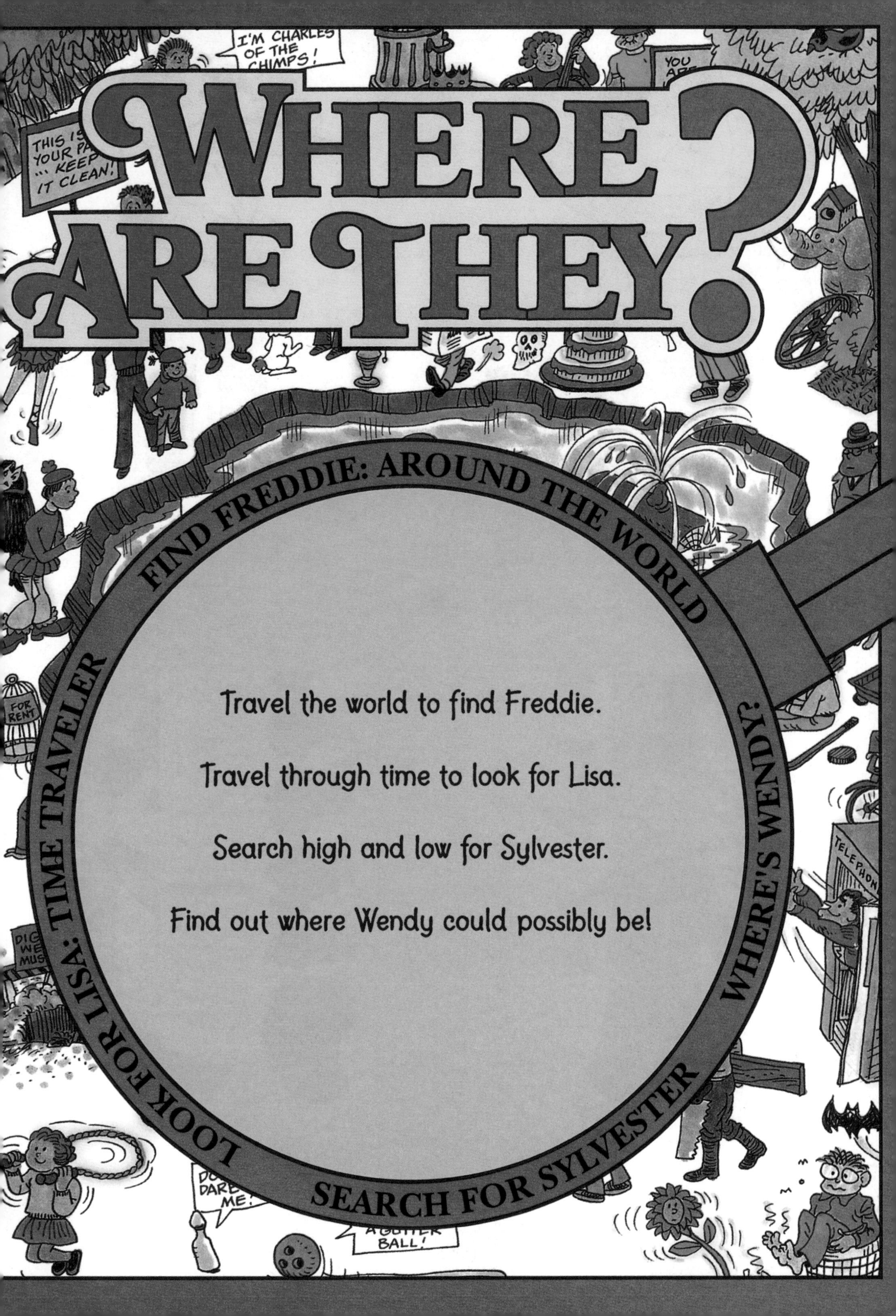

# WHERE ARE THEY?

FIND FREDDIE: AROUND THE WORLD

TIME TRAVELER

LOOK FOR LISA:

SEARCH FOR SYLVESTER

WHERE'S WENDY?

Travel the world to find Freddie.

Travel through time to look for Lisa.

Search high and low for Sylvester.

Find out where Wendy could possibly be!

**FREDDIE**

**LISA**

**WENDY**

**SYLVESTER**

# FIND FREDDIE AROUND THE WORLD

# Find Freddie in the
## United States
### and...

- Alien
- Barbell
- Baseball player
- Beavers (2)
- Binoculars
- Carrot
- Cheese
- Cook
- Doctor
- Dog bone
- Dogs (2)
- Elephant
- Fire hydrant
- Football player
- Ice-cream cone
- Mice (3)
- Movie camera
- Octopus
- Palm trees (4)
- Rabbits (2)
- Skier
- Snake
- Snowman
- Stop sign
- Tent
- Trash can
- White House

# Find Freddie in this **Winter Wonderland** and...

- Balloon
- Banana peel
- Caveman
- Deer
- Dog sled
- Dogs (3)
- Hockey player
- Ice skates (5)
- Leprechaun
- Maple syrup
- Moose
- Periscope
- Police officer
- Pumpkin
- Rabbit
- Raccoon
- Refrigerator
- Sailboat
- Santa Claus
- Skiers (2)
- Spear
- Superhero
- Telescope
- Tent
- Tin man
- Tree stumps (4)
- TV camera

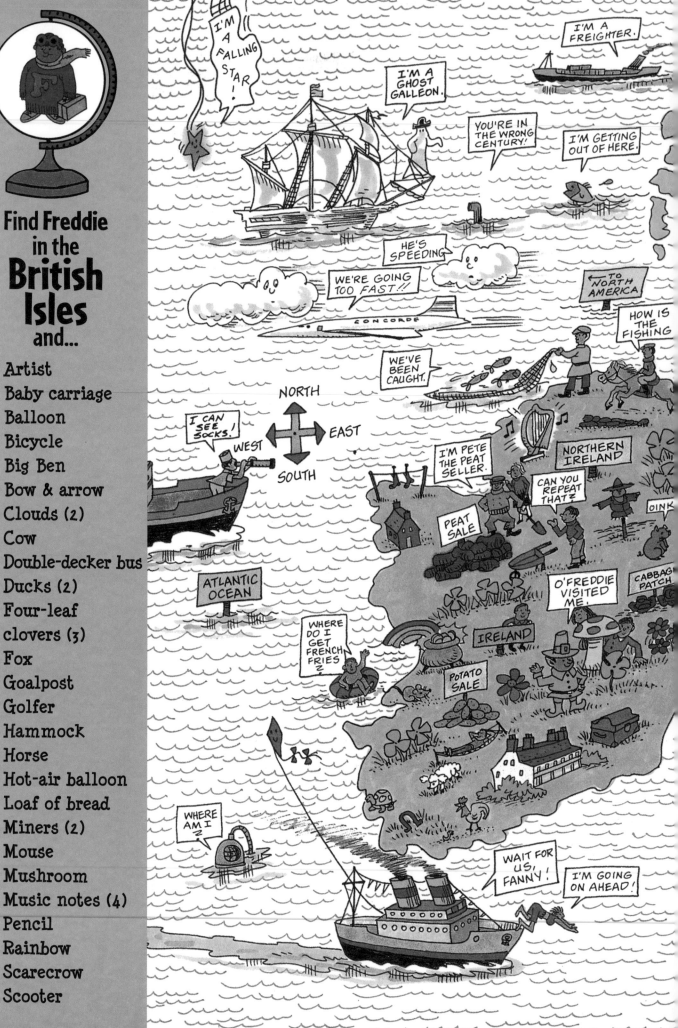

Find Freddie
in the
**British
Isles**
and...

# Find Freddie among these **Friendly Foreigners** and...

- Anchor
- Antlers
- Baby
- Balloon
- Barn
- Bullfighter
- Camera
- Cheese
- Clothespins (4)
- Deer (2)
- Eagle scout
- Eiffel Tower
- Elephant
- Fisherman
- Greek ruins
- Kite
- Oil well
- Owl
- Panda
- Picnic basket
- Piggy bank
- Pyramid
- Rain slicker
- Telescope
- Umbrellas (2)
- Viking
- Windmill

# Find Freddie in this
# Vast and Exotic Land
### and...

- Alligator
- Bigfoot
- Black bear
- Bone
- Camels (2)
- Duck
- Elephant
- Gas pump
- Lion
- Magic carpet
- Mermaid
- Mongoose
- Monkey
- Mount Everest
- Mount Fuji
- Music notes (11)
- Penguin
- Rhinoceros
- Sailboats (2)
- Sheep (2)
- Snowmen (2)
- Soccer ball
- Star
- Suez Canal
- Tea bag
- Umbrella
- Whale

## Find Freddie in this African Adventure-Land and...

- Alligator
- Ant
- Banana
- Bone
- Cat
- Crown
- Diamonds
- Donkey
- Egg
- Fishing nets (2)
- Fishing pole
- Flamingo
- Message in a bottle
- Moon
- Mug
- Mushroom
- Palm trees (3)
- Pyramid
- Rowboats (4)
- Santa Claus
- Seal
- Sunglasses (4)
- Surfboard
- Telescope
- Turtle
- Zebra

# Find Freddie in the Land Down Under and...

- Apples (7)
- Barbecue
- Boot
- Cloud
- Cow
- Crocodile
- Doctor
- Eggs (4)
- Emu
- Fishing poles (2)
- Ghost
- Guitar
- Lifeguard
- Message in a bottle
- Octopus
- Penguin
- Platypus
- Sailboats (2)
- Shark fins (5)
- Skiers (2)
- Snake
- Snowman
- Surfboards (9)
- Tasmanian devil
- Tennis rackets (4)
- Tire

# Find Freddie in this
## Blistery Blizzard
### and...

- Airplane
- Aliens (2)
- Baseball
- Box
- Campfire
- Circus tents (2)
- Easel
- Football
- Heart
- Helicopter
- Ice castle
- Ice skates (6)
- Jack-o'-lantern
- Kangaroo
- Kite
- Magic carpet
- Paintbrush
- Periscope
- Santa Claus
- Skis (4)
- Sleds (5)
- Spaceship
- Stars (2)
- Tennis racket
- Tin man
- Tombstone
- Top hats (2)

# Find Freddie
## in
# South
# America
### and...

- Angel
- Ant
- Banana peel
- Beach ball
- Beehive
- Briefcase
- Candy bar
- Chinchilla
- Coconut
- Condor
- Dracula
- Flamingos (3)
- Flying bats (2)
- Iguana
- Jaguar
- Manatee
- Mouse
- Music notes (3)
- Ostrich
- Penguin
- Pig
- Shark fins (2)
- Skull
- Spider
- Tires (2)
- Top hat
- Toucans (2)

# Find Freddie in Central America and...

- Banana tree
- Birdbath
- Bones (2)
- Broom
- Bucket
- Bull
- Cactus
- Camera
- Flying bats (2)
- Football
- Golfer
- Heart
- Hot-air balloon
- Kite
- Medal
- Periscope
- Pie
- Piggy bank
- Pizza
- Police officer
- Princess
- Rabbits (2)
- Sailboats (4)
- Snakes (2)
- Turtle
- Water skis
- Whale

# Find Freddie on his **Last Stop** and...

- Alarm clock
- Apple
- Baseball player
- Beaver
- Cactus (2)
- Carrot
- Castle
- Cow
- Cowboys (2)
- Dogs (3)
- Hose
- Mermaid
- Moose
- Octopus
- Painted egg
- Paper airplane
- Parachute
- Periscope
- Refrigerator
- Sailboats (2)
- Sherlock Holmes
- Skunk
- Snowball
- Suit of armor
- Tents (2)
- Trash can
- Whales (2)
- Witch

# Find Freddie and...

| | | | |
|---|---|---|---|
| Apple | Fire hydrant | Ice-cream cone | Pencil |
| Baseball bat | Flower | Jump rope | Pizza box |
| Birdcage | Football helmet | Medal | Plate |
| Bucket | Frog | Mitten | Rocking chair |
| Candle | Gift | Moon | Turtle |
| Cupcake | Hearts (2) | Mouse | |

# LOOK FOR LISA: TIME TRAVELER

# Look for Lisa in Prehistoric Times and...

- Baby carriage
- Candle
- Cherry
- Clothespin
- Dinosaur egg
- Faucet
- Four-leaf clover
- Hammer
- Hot chocolate
- Life preserver
- Message in a bottle
- Necklace
- Necktie
- "No U Turn"
- Palm trees (2)
- Periscope
- Piggy bank
- Pizza
- Ring
- Scarecrow
- Skateboard
- Stars (2)
- Swimming duck
- Tire
- Toothbrush
- Volcanoes (2)
- Wooden wheel

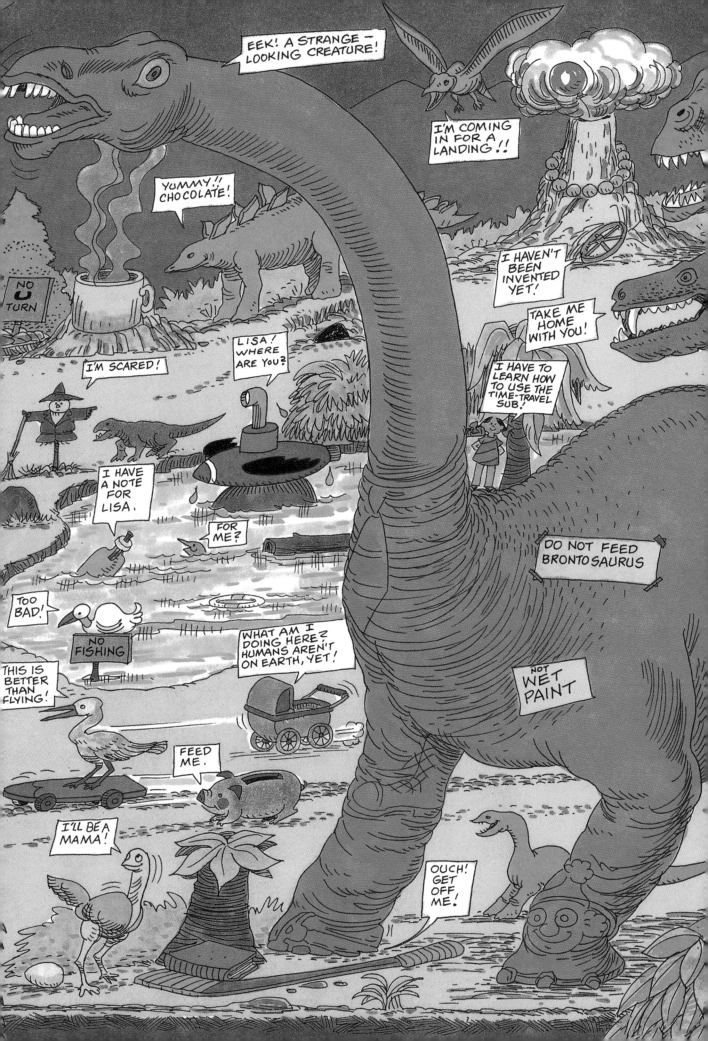

## Look for Lisa in the Creepy Castle and...

- Apples (2)
- Arrow
- Ball and chain
- Balloon
- Banana peel
- Baseball cap
- Birdcage
- Bones (6)
- Bowling pin
- Broom
- Calendar
- Carrot
- Crayon
- Door knocker
- Flying bats (3)
- Football
- Ghost
- Jar
- Lantern
- Mice (5)
- Nail
- Oil can
- Paintbrush
- Pencil
- Rose
- Scissors
- Wristwatch
- Yo-yo

## Look for Lisa at this Historic Happening and...

## Look for Lisa as she **Rocks and Rolls** and...

Look for **Lisa** among these **Exciting Experiments** and...

## Look for Lisa in these
# Cavernous Craters
### and...

# Look for **Lisa** in the **Ocean** and...

- Baby
- Barrel
- Baseball bat
- Basketball
- Boot
- Bucket
- Captain's hat
- Elephant
- Fish (3)
- Guitar
- Harp
- Heart
- Homework
- Hot-air balloon
- Ice-cream cone
- Key
- Oars (5)
- Painting
- Palm tree
- Scuba diver
- Shark fins (2)
- Slice of watermelon
- Sock
- Surfer
- Television
- Tin can
- Tire
- Tree

## Look for **Lisa** at this **Special Celebration** and...

- Axe
- Barrel
- Basketball
- Bear
- Boat
- Book
- Bowling ball
- Chef
- Duck
- Ears of corn (2)
- Feather
- Fish
- Handkerchief
- Magnifying glass
- Mouse
- Owl
- Paintbrush
- Pizza delivery
- Pumpkins (3)
- Smoke signals
- Spoon
- Telephone
- Tepees (2)
- Turkeys (2)
- Turtle
- Watering can
- Wedding cake
- Worm

# Look for Lisa at
# Thomas Edison's Lab
## and...

- Bandanas (5)
- Birdcage
- Briefcase
- Cat
- Chairs (2)
- Clipboards (2)
- Club
- Cookies
- Cowboy hats (4)
- Curtains
- Eyeglasses
- Film projector
- Fish
- Hammer
- Pail
- Periscope
- Picture
- Plant
- Poodle
- Rain slicker
- Roller skates
- Sailboat
- Screwdriver
- Shadow
- Sheep
- Trash can
- Triangle
- Turtle

# Look for **Lisa** among these **Friendly Aliens** and...

# Look for Lisa at the Magic Show and...

# Look for Lisa and...

| | | | |
|---|---|---|---|
| Baseball bat | Cane | Moon | Sun |
| Bird | Fire hydrant | Octopus | Tire |
| Bottle | Fish | Rabbit | Top hat |
| Broom | Flowers (2) | Saw | Turtle |
| Cactus | Hammers (2) | Scarves (2) | Wreath |
| Can | Kite | Snake | |

# Search for Sylvester at this Mad Mall and...

- Astronaut
- Balloon
- Barber pole
- Bone
- Bride
- Briefcase
- Cat
- Cowboy hat
- Feathers (2)
- Fish (2)
- King
- Ladder
- Manhole
- Moon
- Mouse
- Music note
- Parachute
- Pizza
- Robin Hood
- Sailboat
- Scarecrow
- Shopping bag
- Skier
- Stool
- Stuffed elephant
- Tin man
- Top hat
- Winter hats (2)

# Search for **Sylvester** in this **Fun-Filled Playground** and...

- Arrows (3)
- Ballerina
- Banana peel
- Beach ball
- Birdcage
- Birdhouse
- Birds (4)
- Bowling pin
- Cactus
- Cannon
- Diploma
- Dracula
- Ducklings (4)
- Eight ball
- Fire hydrant
- Flying bat
- Hockey stick
- Lamp
- Newspapers (2)
- Paint bucket
- Police officer
- Propeller hat
- Rooster
- Saws (2)
- Shovel
- Superhero
- Turtle

# Search for **Sylvester** at the **Zany Zoo** and...

- Baseball bat
- Baseball caps (4)
- Bow tie
- Camel
- Fish
- Football
- Girl with pigtails
- Kangaroo
- Little Red Riding Hood
- Neckties (3)
- Owl
- Parrot
- Pig
- Pine tree
- Rabbit
- Raccoon
- Scarf
- School bus
- Sea horse
- Seal
- Shovel
- Spoon
- Telescope
- Top hat
- Toy turtle
- Trash can
- Turtle

Search for **Sylvester** in this **Alphabetical School** and...

A
B
C
D
E
F
G
H
I
J
K
L
M
N
O
P
Q
R
S
T
U
V
W
X
Y
Z

# Search for **Sylvester** at the **Basketball Game** and...

- Alligator
- Balloons (2)
- Banana peel
- Baseball
- Bowling ball
- Cannon
- Cherry
- Envelopes (2)
- Eyeglasses (2)
- Football helmet
- Ghost
- Headbands (2)
- Hot dog
- Jack-o'-lantern
- Kangaroo
- Kite
- Lost glove
- Pail
- Pencil
- Pizza box
- Police officer
- Pom poms (4)
- Rabbit
- Snake
- Stars (3)
- Tarzan
- Turtle

# Search for Sylvester at this Spooky Mansion and...

- Arrows (2)
- Book
- Brush
- Bucket
- Candle
- Carrot
- Cauldron
- Curtains
- Flower
- Flying bat
- Football
- Ghost
- Hammer
- Lawn mower
- Letter
- Old tire
- Piano keys
- Shovel
- Skulls (2)
- Spiderweb
- Sword
- Tin can
- Trash can lid
- Vulture
- Wagon
- Watering can
- Witch

# Search for Sylvester at Detective Donald's Digs and...

# Search for Sylvester at this Silly Circus and...

- Balloon with star
- Barrel
- Cactus
- Cake
- Camel
- Cannon
- Clothespins (3)
- Clowns (4)
- Crayon
- Firefighter
- Flowerpot
- Light bulb
- Mice (2)
- Necktie
- Party hat
- Pinocchio
- Pizza
- Police officer
- Skateboard
- Snowman
- Spoon
- Stars (5)
- Teacup
- Tin man
- Unicycle
- Witch
- Wizard hat
- Worm

## Search for Sylvester as he Soars Through the Sky and...

- Ape
- Banana
- Baseball bat
- Bathtub
- Bird
- Bow
- Carrot
- Cupcake
- Fishermen (2)
- Flowers (4)
- Flying bat
- Football player
- Guitar
- Moon
- Pot
- Scarecrow
- Scarf
- Shovel
- Spaceship
- Stars (3)
- Sunglasses
- Target
- Teapot
- Tent
- TV antenna
- Watering can
- Witch

## Search for Sylvester in Bamboo Town and...

- Balloons (2)
- Brooms (2)
- Drum
- Eyeglasses (2)
- Fire hydrants (2)
- Football
- Football player
- Ghost
- Gift
- Hard hats (2)
- Heart
- Horseshoe
- Ice-cream cones (2)
- Jump rope
- Kangaroo
- Knight
- Mask
- Medal
- Octopus
- Pencil
- Periscope
- Record
- Socks (3)
- Stool
- Straw
- Telescope

# Search for Sylvester and...

| | | | |
|---|---|---|---|
| Apple | Carrot | Football | Paintbrush |
| Bamboo shoot | Cupcake | Horn | Screwdriver |
| Baseball | Drum | Kite | Spoon |
| Bone | Fire hydrant | Leaf | Top hat |
| Candle | Flag | Lock | Turtle |
| Cane | Flowers (10) | Moon | |

# Find Wendy at Witchville High School and...

- Apple
- Axe
- Baseball bat
- Bear
- Bell
- Blimp
- Bowling ball
- Cauldrons (2)
- Dog
- Flying bats (2)
- Football
- Green hand
- Headless man
- Mask
- Mushrooms (3)
- One-eyed monsters (2)
- Pencil
- Piece of paper
- Scarecrow
- Shovel
- Skateboard
- Tire
- Tombstones (3)
- Turtle
- TV antenna
- Unicorn
- Walking tree

# Find Wendy in the **Classroom** and...

- Baseball bat
- Bell
- Bones (2)
- Books (6)
- Broken egg
- Button
- Clock
- Eight ball
- Eyeglasses (2)
- Flying bats (2)
- Football
- Hourglass
- Ice-cream cone
- Jack-o'-lantern
- Key
- Magic wand
- Marshmallow
- Needle
- Octopus
- Piece of chalk
- Pizza
- Rabbit
- Saw
- Scissors
- Skeleton
- Skunk
- Stool
- Straw
- Umbrella

# Find Wendy on the
## Witches'
## Class Trip
### and...

- Apple
- Basket
- Basketball
- Bird
- Cactus
- Chair
- Chicken
- Crayon
- Crocodile
- Dogs (2)
- Faucet
- Flowers (2)
- Flying bat
- Football
- Hammer
- Hearts (2)
- Hockey stick
- Ice-cream cone
- Mitten
- Paintbrush
- Paint bucket
- Painted egg
- Periscope
- Pizza slice
- Squirrel
- Sunglasses (2)
- Top hat
- Watermelon slice

# Find Wendy in the
# **Lunchroom**
### and...

- Apple
- Bird
- Broken nose
- Cactus
- Candle
- Cat
- Chick
- Cookbook
- Crystal ball
- Cymbals (2)
- Drum
- Flower
- Football
- Frying pans (3)
- Graduate
- Lighthouse
- Music notes (3)
- Paper airplane
- Plate of cookies
- Santa Claus
- Skull
- Snakes (2)
- Straw
- Teapot
- Trash can
- Turtle
- Volcano
- Yellow hand
- Yellow sock

## Look for **Wendy** during **Final Exams** and...

# Hunt for Wendy
## at
# **Graduation**
### and...

- Barbell
- Bones (2)
- Broken mirror
- Brooms (3)
- Can
- Candle
- Cracked egg
- Dog
- Drum
- Flying bats (2)
- Ghost
- Graduation cap
- Guitar
- Kite
- Marshmallow
- Moons (2)
- Music note
- Panda
- Pumpkins (2)
- Robot
- Sled
- Target
- Tire
- Tombstones (13)
- Toolbox
- Turtle
- Umbrella
- Wizard
- Worm

# Find Wendy in
# Count Dracula's Living Room
### and...

## Search for **Wendy** in **Dr. Frankenstein's Laboratory** and...

# Hunt for Wendy in the Mummy's Tomb and...

- "1st Prize" ribbon
- Bell
- Butterfly
- Cactus
- Cherry
- Cracked pot
- Duck
- Fire hydrant
- Fish
- Giraffe
- Key
- Lion
- Lobster
- Moon
- Mouse
- Painted egg
- Ring
- Rooster
- Sea horse
- Seal
- Spiderweb
- Tepee
- Tiger
- Top hat
- Trunk
- Yellow bird
- Watering can
- Winter hat

# Find Wendy on the Jack-O'-Lantern Farm and...

- Apple
- Baseball bat
- Birds (2)
- Bones (2)
- Bowling ball
- Cactus
- Carrot
- Egg
- Fat candle
- Fire hydrant
- Flashlight
- Frog
- Ghosts (2)
- Hoe
- Kangaroo
- Lawn mower
- Lollipop
- Lost boot
- Magnifying glass
- Mailbox
- Mask
- Mummy
- Pear
- Periscope
- Pig
- Rake
- Skunk
- Surfboard

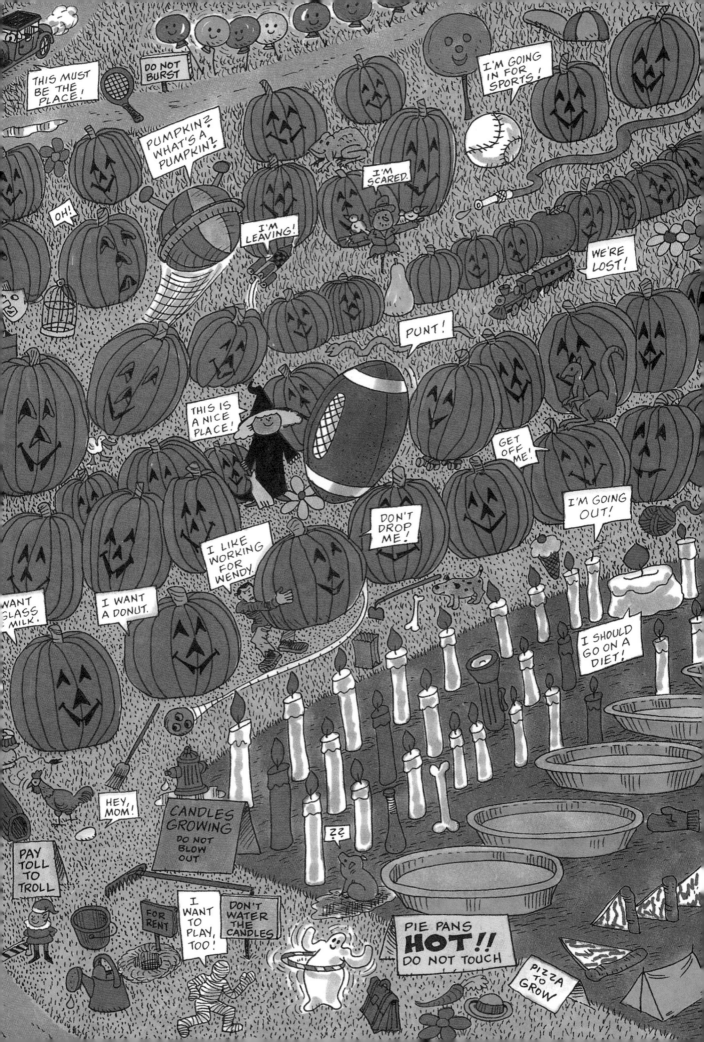

All of Wendy's
"Where Are They?"
friends have come to visit
her jack-o'-lantern farm.

## Look for:

- Bone
- Boot
- Brooms (3)
- Candy cane
- Chicken
- Crayon
- Flowers (2)
- Heart
- Mouse
- Mushroom
- Nail
- Smallest
  jack-o'-lantern

**WHERE'S WENDY?**

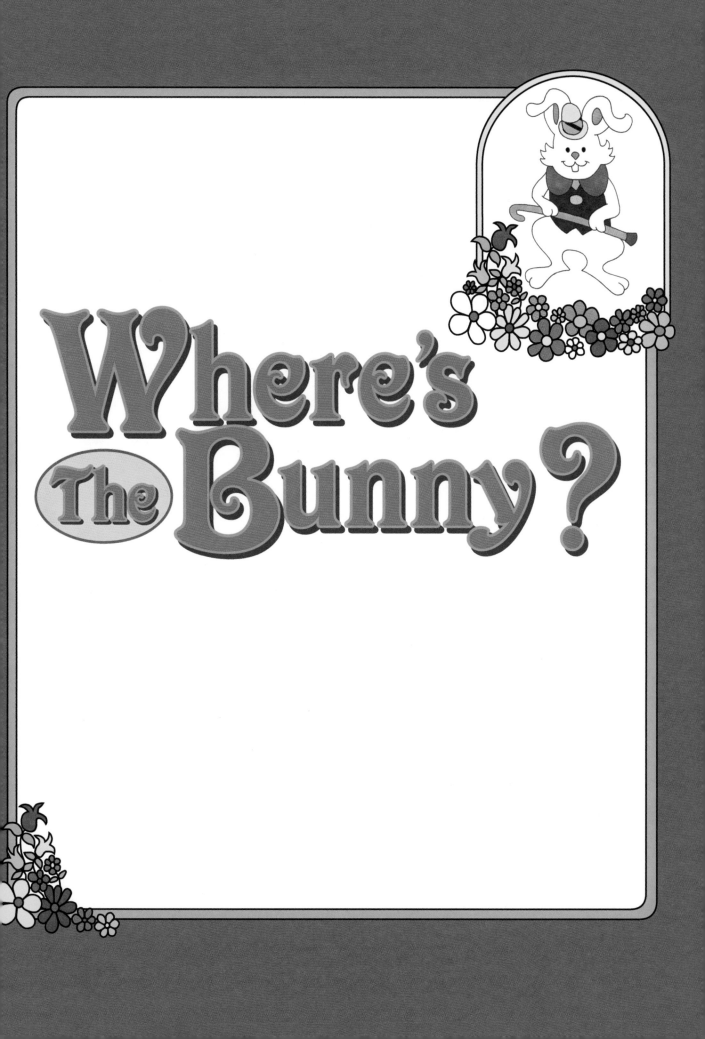

# Find Bunny Honey at Wacky Farms and...

- Blackboard
- Bow ties (2)
- Bucket
- Burst balloon
- Cat
- Chickens (2)
- Cow
- Donkey
- Elephant
- Firefighter
- Fire hydrants (5)
- Flying balloon
- Flying bat
- Football player
- Ghost
- Giraffe
- Mouse
- Pencil
- Rocking chair
- Sailboats (4)
- Santa Claus
- Shovel
- Spaghetti
- Sunglasses
- Top hats (4)
- Truck tires (4)
- Turtle
- Umbrellas (2)

# Find Bunny Honey at the Costume Party and...

- Apple
- Arrow
- Barrel
- Basket
- Beaver
- Bells (2)
- Broom
- Cactus (2)
- Clothespin
- Coffeepot
- Crown
- Ear of corn
- Egg
- Football
- Fork
- Frog
- Headless dancer
- Hot dog
- Ice-cream pop
- Ice skate
- Kite
- Lollipop
- Magnifying glass
- Pencils (2)
- Pizza
- Roller skates
- Skateboards (2)
- Tepee

# Find Bunny Honey in the Bunny Parade and...

- ○ Accordion
- ○ Bagpipes
- ○ Banjo
- ○ Birdcage
- ○ Bone
- ○ Boomerang
- ○ Bowling ball
- ○ Candy cane
- ○ Carrots (11)
- ○ Chocolate bunny
- ○ Clown
- ○ Covered wagon
- ○ Drums (3)
- ○ Flowerpot
- ○ Ghost
- ○ Guitar
- ○ Harp
- ○ Jack-o'-lantern
- ○ Knight
- ○ Light bulbs (2)
- ○ Mouse
- ○ Mummy
- ○ Owl
- ○ Painted eggs (12)
- ○ Paper airplane
- ○ Skateboard
- ○ Sled
- ○ Snowman

# Find **Bunny Honey** at the **Factory** and...

- Apple
- Arrow
- Baseball bat
- Basketball
- Birds (6)
- Black jelly beans (3)
- Candle
- Carrot
- Chimney
- Clothespins (2)
- Fish
- Flower
- Football player
- Handbag
- Igloo
- Knight
- Lost shoe
- Monster
- Pencil
- Pig
- Referee
- Snake
- Spear
- Top hat
- Turtle
- Umbrella
- Vacuum cleaner

# Find **Bunny Honey** at the **Honey Bunny** **Hotel** and...

- Balloons (3)
- Basketball
- Bowling ball
- Burned-out light
- Cactus
- Carrots (3)
- Chef
- Crack in egg
- Diving board
- Elephant
- Fish
- Frog
- Giraffe
- Jack-o'-lantern
- Ladders (3)
- Lifeguard
- Mouse
- Painter
- Parachute
- Periscope
- Pole vaulter
- Santa bunny
- Scarecrow
- Skateboard
- Snake
- Star
- Telescope
- Tree

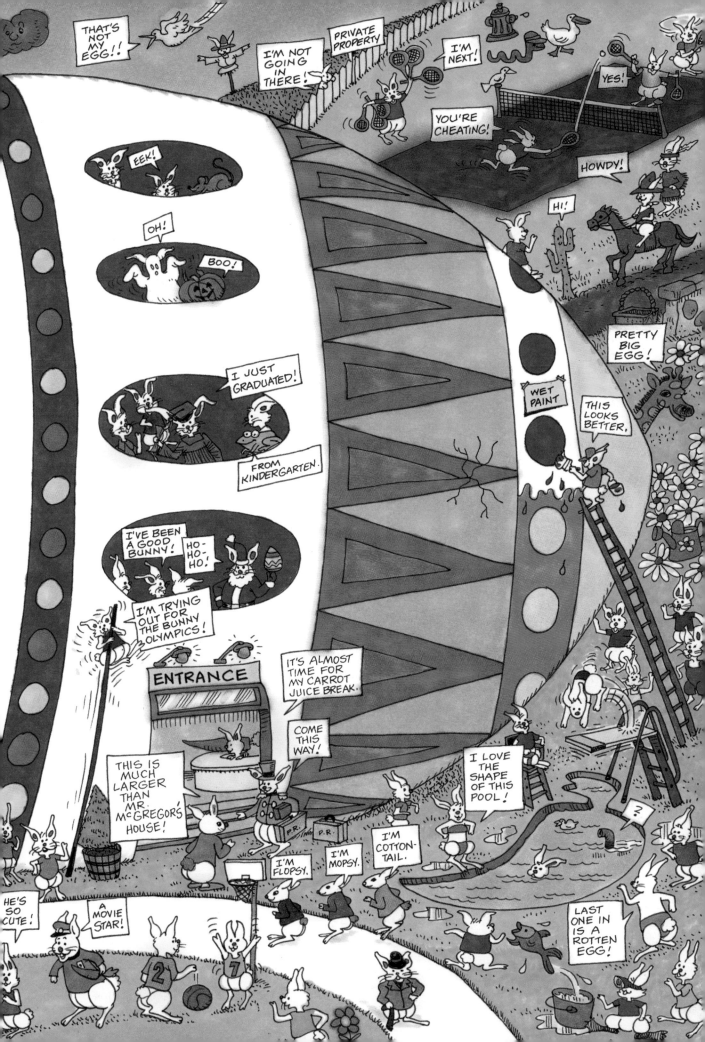

# Find **Bunny Honey** on the **Bunny Trail** and...

- Apple
- Arrow
- Baskets (2)
- Bat
- Bell
- Bone
- Book
- Chimney
- Clock
- Crocodile
- Cup
- Drum
- Flowerpot
- Flying carpet
- Ghost
- Heart
- Helicopter
- Ice-cream cone
- Palm tree
- Rooster
- Sheep
- Ship in a bottle
- Sled
- Surfer
- Toaster
- Turtle
- Umbrella
- Wagon

# Find Bunny Honey at the
## Daisy
## Maze
### and...

- Airplane
- Apple
- Arrow
- Balloon
- Baseball bat
- Basket
- Bee
- Bone
- Camel
- Cap
- Carrot
- Clown
- Elephant
- Fish (2)
- Frog
- Helicopter
- Igloo
- Monster
- Pencil
- Ring
- Schoolbag
- Shovel
- Snail
- Snake
- Snowman
- Sock
- Squirrel
- Sunglasses

# Find Bunny Honey at the Great Egg Roll and...

- Ant
- Bee
- Clothespin
- Dogs (2)
- Duck
- Elephant
- Feather
- Fish
- Flamingo
- Football
- Fried egg
- Frog
- Helmet
- Horse
- Kangaroo
- Kite
- Magnifying glass
- Meatballs
- Paintbrush
- Raccoon
- Rhinoceros
- Scarves (2)
- Seal
- Skateboard
- Snake
- Spaceship
- Sunglasses
- Top hat

## Find Bunny Honey at the
# Spring Sale
## and...

- Arrow
- Astronaut
- Banana peel
- Basket
- Birdcage
- Boxing glove
- Cactus
- Candle
- Centipede
- Chef
- Clothespin
- Clown
- Crown
- Fishing pole
- Flowerpot
- Ghost
- Horse
- Humpty Dumpty
- Igloo
- Lamp
- Monkey
- Mouse
- Octopus
- Owl
- Pies (2)
- Pirate
- Police officer
- Rooster

# Find **Bunny Honey** in the
# Great Outdoors
## and...

- Arrow
- Balloon
- Birds (3)
- Boots (3)
- Envelope
- Flying bat
- Football helmet
- Heart
- Hockey stick
- Horseshoe
- Ice skate
- Key
- Mitten
- Mushrooms (3)
- Periscope
- Pocketknife
- Pocket watch
- Roller skates
- Sailboat
- Scarf
- Skateboard
- Sled
- Star
- Tepee
- Unicorn
- Watering can
- Wooden fish
- Wooden rabbit

# Find Bunny Honey in Fairy-tale Land and...

- Arrow
- Banana peel
- Bell
- Broom
- Bucket
- Cactus
- Candle
- Comb
- Cooking pot
- Dog
- Earring
- Firecracker
- Golf club
- Hearts (2)
- "Ho-ho-ho!"
- Kangaroo
- Moose
- Muffin man
- Painted egg
- Paper bag
- Saw
- Screwdriver
- Seesaw
- Shovel
- Slipper
- Sneakers
- Star
- Toothbrush

# Find **Bunny Honey** at the **Playground** and...

- Alien creature
- Balloons (2)
- Barbecue grill
- Baseball glove
- Binoculars
- Boat
- Books (2)
- Candle
- Cat
- Chef's hat
- Dart
- Fish (2)
- Frog
- Heart
- Helmets (2)
- Lost mittens (3)
- Mask
- Model airplane
- Monster
- Mouse
- Mushroom
- Nail
- Nest
- Owl
- Paper airplane
- Sailor hat
- Schoolbag
- Soccer ball

# Find Bunny Honey at this
# Snowman Meltdown
### and...

- Baseball
- Birds (4)
- Broom
- Butterfly
- Cage
- Candy cane
- Clown
- Drum
- Duck
- Fire hydrant
- Ghost
- Hammer
- Heart
- Hockey puck
- Jack-o'-lantern
- Key
- Kite
- Lollipop
- Milk container
- Pig
- Roller skater
- Rooster
- Sleeping cat
- Sock
- Stars (2)
- Sunglasses (2)
- Worm
- Wreath

# Find Bunny Honey in this Zany Egg Contest and...

- Arrow
- Balloon
- Bear
- Books (3)
- Cat
- Chick
- Cup
- Dog
- Fallen leaf
- Feather
- Fish
- Flowerpot
- Flying bat
- Frying pan
- Ghost
- Horseshoe
- Key
- Kite
- Magnifying glass
- Neckties (2)
- Paper airplane
- Pencil
- Star
- Toothbrush
- Tree stump
- Turtle
- Zebra

# Find Bunny Honey in the Boucing Babies **Field** and...

- Alarm clock
- Baby bird
- Baby deer
- Baby elephants (2)
- Baby fish (2)
- Baby giraffe
- Baby human
- Baby kangaroo
- Baby mice (2)
- Baby monkey
- Baby owl
- Baby rabbits (3)
- Baby squirrel
- Baby turtles (2)
- Baby whale
- Baby worm
- Bone
- Books (2)
- Bowling pin
- Chicks (2)
- Ducklings (2)
- Eggs (5)
- Hang glider
- Kittens (3)
- Lamb
- Piglets (2)
- Puppies (2)